Once Upon a
Princess

by Barbara Berg

Illustrated by Andrew J St. Angelo

Once Upon A Princess

Written by Barbara Berg

Illustrated by Andrew J. St. Angelo

ISBN: 978-1-955468-01-5 (Paperback edition)
ISBN: 978-1-955468-00-8 (Hardcover edition)

Published by: IQ Media Press Corp.

Dedication

To my father and my cousin Leona, who always knew what to say, and more importantly, how to listen.

-- Barbara

To my wife, Tammy, and our princesses, Carly and Erin, for their inspiration, encouragement and love.

-- Andrew

Once upon a time
Many years ago
In a kingdom far away
Beyond the rain and snow,

There lived a pretty princess
Her beauty far renowned
Who wasn't able to convey
A single thought in sound.

To whisper or to cry
To hiccup, even snore,
To the princess it was all
Just too much to endure.

The doctors at the palace
Tried their very best
To cure the pretty princess
But finally confessed,

"It's our sad conviction
No remedy we've found
Will cure such an affliction
And help her make a sound."

The king and queen
were quite distressed,

They'd every right to be.

They issued a sincere request
By means of this decree.

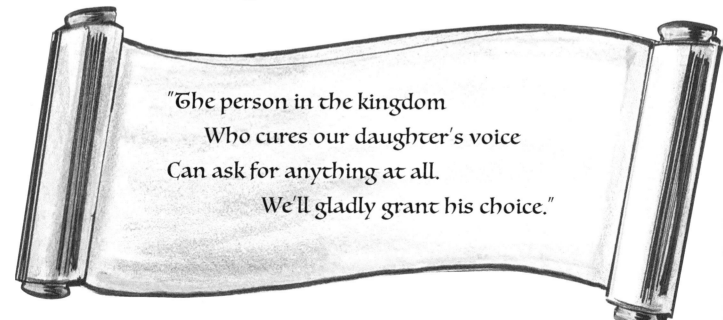

"The person in the kingdom
Who cures our daughter's voice
Can ask for anything at all.
We'll gladly grant his choice."

All across the nation in every village green
They read the proclamation sent by the king and queen.

And everyone who listened just could not agree
On how to cure the princess and earn the tempting fee.

"It's all in her mind," some folks said.
"She should be confined to her regal bed."

"We won't let her leave
 Her chambers until
 We really believe
 She's no longer ill."

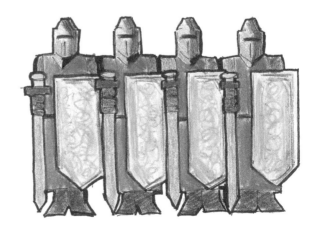

Some of the citizens correctly thought,
A better solution ought to be sought.

There were those who were sure
That the road to success
Was a medical cure
For the silent princess.

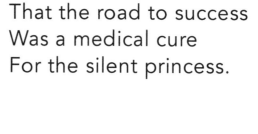

"Some medication or vaccination,
Rehabilitation or perhaps, a long vacation."

"We'll certainly cure the princess' disease.
Then we'll collect any fee that we please."

The self made doctors gathered from every corner of the land.
Though why the princess never spoke, no one could understand.

One man, hoping that she'd scream
Prepared a scary sight.
Not a sound emerged, though she
Was shivering with fright.

To make her laugh,
    They tickled her toes.
To make her sneeze
    They tickled her nose.

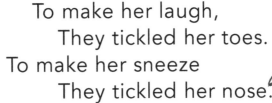

A cup of tea with sugar,
Lemon juice with honey,
Chicken soup and medicine
That tasted very funny.

The princess tasted all of these, but all to no avail,
For every remedy she tried was hopeless, doomed to fail.

Finally a lad arrived
At the palace grounds
Who didn't come to cure the girl
And help her utter sounds.

For he had had enough of girls
Who chattered in his ear.
He yearned to meet a quiet girl
To love, but not to hear.

And he'd been told,
In every city
That she was kind
As well as pretty.

So naturally,
The young man tried
To win the princess
For his bride.

But when he told the king and queen about his bold new plan,
They didn't know what they should think of such a strange
   young man.

The king was hoping that he'd have a daughter who could speak.
Instead, he found a son-in-law he didn't even seek.

So rather than accept the lad, the king finally said:
"After you have cured my girl, I'll gladly let you wed."

To this, the bold young man replied:
"Your Royal Highnesses,
If I may, I'd like to try
To cure her with my kisses."

The king's face turned a fiery red.
The queen became quite pale.
After what the young man said,
He should be locked up in jail.

The king then ordered that the lad
Be chased out of the court.
If he ever dared return,
He'd have his head cut short.

This was not the way to serve the king's own family.
The bold young man did not deserve to see Her Majesty.

But one of the physicians
Whispered to the king:
"Why not let the young man try,
For we've tried everything."

"And if this handsome young man's kiss
Restores you daughter's voice,
If he can accomplish this,
The kingdom will rejoice."

"The worst thing that could happen
Is that his plan would fail.
Then execute the brazen lad
Or lock him up in jail."

"The lad will be a hero
In the common people's eyes.
The man who works this miracle
They'll surely idolize."

"Then when they will finally wed,
We can all celebrate.
A hero for a princess
Would make the perfect mate."

The king accepted the advice of the court physician.
The lad could kiss the princess twice with the king's permission.

"If she's still silent when you kiss," the king trembled with dread.
"You'll ne'er repeat a word of this, for I shall have your head!"

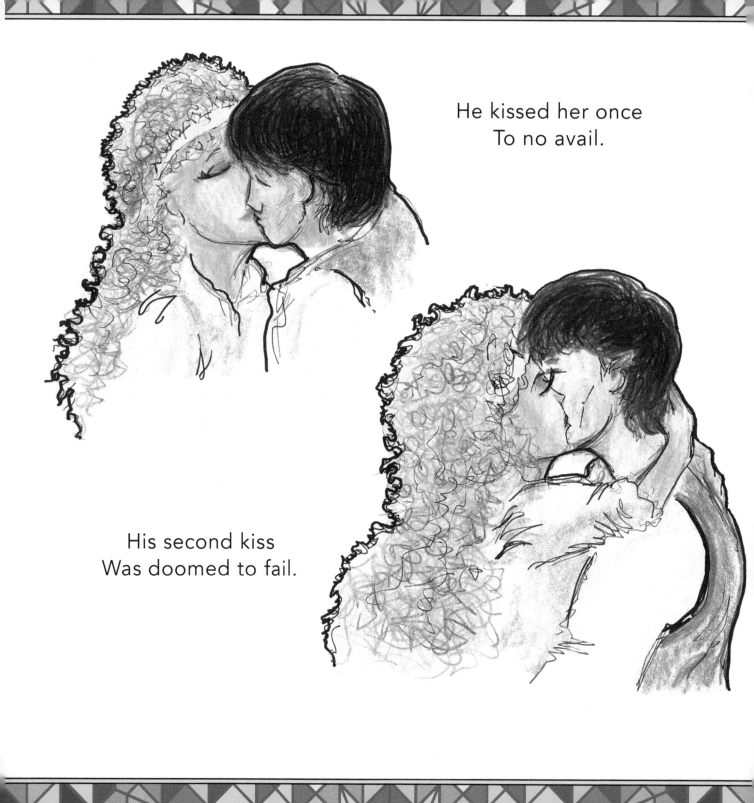

He kissed her once
To no avail.

His second kiss
Was doomed to fail.

The sentence of His Majesty
Condemned the lad to die.
But just before he lost his head...
He heard the princess cry.

"Father, don't behead the lad
For he has claimed my heart.
And I can't bear, because of me,
He and his head must part."

Her parents, they were overjoyed.
From that momentous date,
When she had something good to say,
She didn't hesitate.

They wed that very afternoon.
The preacher asked, "Do you?"

The princess spoke up
Loud and clear
And answered,

"Yes, I do!"

The moral of this fairy tale is

"Speak up when you should.

The right word spoken just in time

Can do a lot of good."

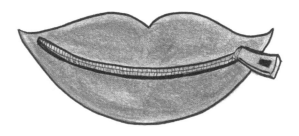

CPSIA information can be obtained
at www.ICGtesting.com
Printed in the USA
LVHW071201280721
693891LV00002B/14